VISTAS

An Interactive Course in English

WORKBOOK

1

Project Director   H. Douglas Brown

Contributing Writer
Marjorie Fuchs

Longman

Publisher: Tina B. Carver
Manager of Product Development: Mary Vaughn
Senior Editor: Larry Anger
Senior Development Editor: Nancy L. Leonhardt
Development Editor: Louisa B. Hellegers
Managing Editor, Production: Sylvia Moore
Senior Production Editor: Tünde A. Dewey
Senior Production Editor: Janet S. Johnston
Design Director: Janet Schmid
Interior and Cover Design: Suzanne Bennett
Pre-Press Buyer: Ray Keating
Manufacturing Buyer: Lori Bulwin
Scheduler: Leslie Coward

Illustrators: Cathy Braffet, Glenn Davis, Don Martinetti,
      Alex Mizuno, Chris Reed, Ellen Sasaki, Arnold Ten
Cover Photo: Wm. Ervin/ Comstock

Printed in the United States of America

18 17 16 15 14 13 12

ISBN   0-13-650342-X

CONTENTS

1 Hello and goodbye

Complete the balloons with the correct expressions from the box.

Goodbye.	Good evening.	Good morning.
Good night.	Hello.	See you tomorrow.

2 The students, the teacher, and the alphabet

A. Match the names and the pictures.

b 1. Mrs. Brennan

____ 2. Keiko

____ 3. Lucy

____ 4. Lynn

____ 5. Oscar

____ 6. Tetsuo

____ 7. Roberto

____ 8. Tony

____ 9. Pravit

____ 10. Yon Mi

B. Correct the spelling test.

	Spelling		English 101
1.	~~goddby~~ goodbye	6.	good evning
2.	student	7.	tommorow
3.	teecher	8.	hello
4.	name	9.	afternon
5.	goodnight	10.	see

3 The classroom

Label each picture. Use the words in the box.

notebook	clock	window
umbrella	handbag	piece of chalk
desk	pen	briefcase

1. *desk*

2. _____

3. _____

4. _____

5. _____

6. _____

7. _____

8. _____

9. _____

4 Useful phrases

Match the sentences and the pictures.

_d_ 1. Listen.

___ 2. Say your name.

___ 3. Close your book.

___ 4. Could you repeat that, please?

___ 5. Ask your partner.

___ 6. I don't know.

___ 7. Write the question.

___ 8. Open your book.

5 Occupations

What's his or her occupation?

1. _an architect_

2. _____

3. _____

4. _____

5. _____

6. _____

7. _____

8. _____

9. _____

10. _____

6 Cardinal numbers

Write the numbers.

1. _twenty_

2. _____

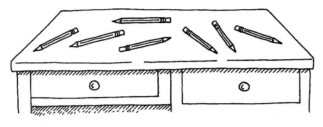

3. _____

4. _____

5. _____

6. _____

7. _____

8. _____

9. _____

10. _____

7 The United States and Canada

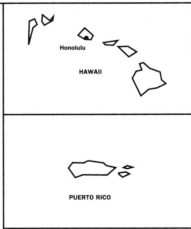

Complete the sentences.

1. There are fifty states in _the United States_ .

2. Boston is in the state of _____ .

3. New York City is in the state of _____ .

4. _____ is in the state of Illinois.

5. _____ and Houston are in _____ .

6. Miami is in _____ .

7. Honolulu is in _____ .

8. Los Angeles, _____ , and San Francisco are in _____ .

9. There are eleven provinces in _____ .

10. Toronto is in the province of _____ .

11. Quebec City is in the province of _____ .

12. Vancouver is in _____ .

8 The world

Match the words and the maps.

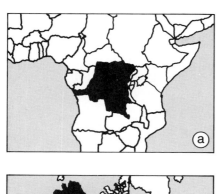 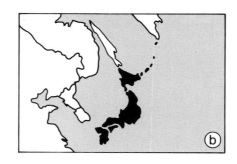 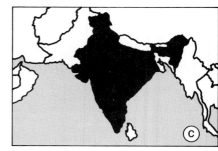

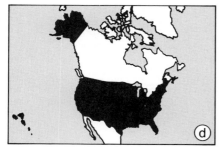 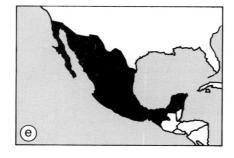 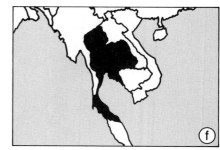

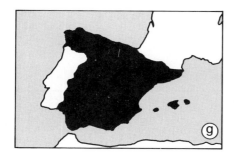  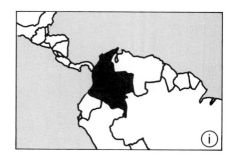

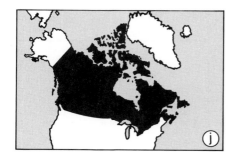 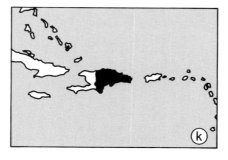 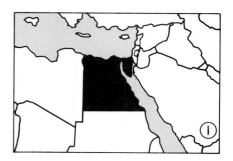

d 1. The United States

___ 2. Spain

___ 3. Zaïre

___ 4. Japan

___ 5. India

___ 6. Mexico

___ 7. Thailand

___ 8. The Dominican
Republic

___ 9. Egypt

___ 10. Colombia

___ 11. Canada

___ 12. Brazil

9 Colors and clothes

A. Label each picture. Use the words in the box.

a blouse	a sock	pants
a tie	a belt	a shirt
a jacket	sunglasses	shorts

1. *a sock*

2. _____

3. _____

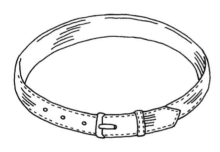

4. _____

5. _____

6. _____

7. _____

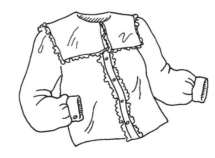

8. _____

9. _____

B. Look at page 10 in your book. Fill in the colors.

1. The pants are *black* .

2. The T-shirt is _____ .

3. The suit is _____ .

4. The skirt is _____ .

5. The shirt is _____ .

6. The shorts are _____ .

10 The house

Label the rooms and the furniture.

bathtub

bathroom

11 Ann Brennan's family

Complete the sentences. Use the words in the box.

brother	husband
daughter	mother
father	sister
grandfather	son
grandmother	wife

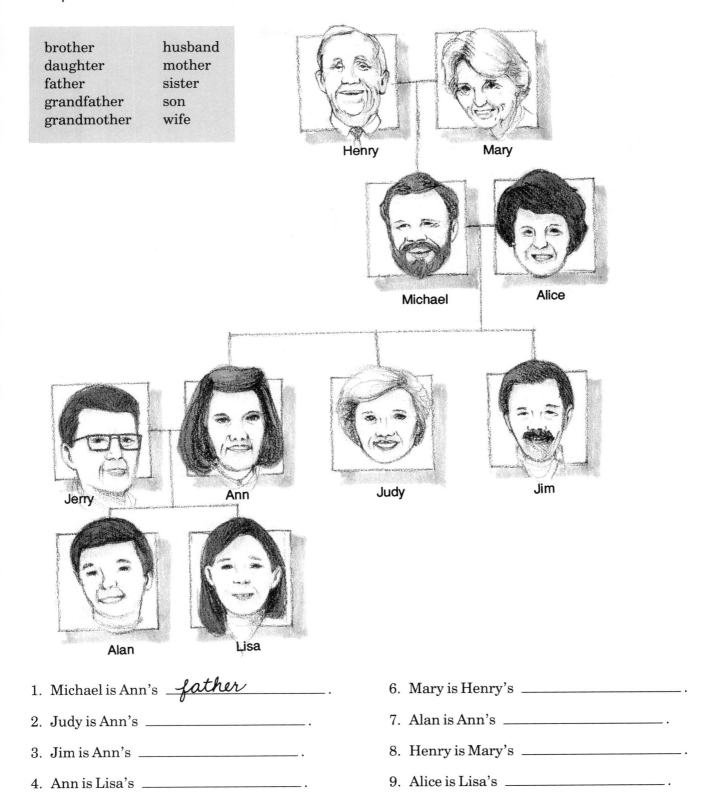

1. Michael is Ann's *father*.

2. Judy is Ann's _____.

3. Jim is Ann's _____.

4. Ann is Lisa's _____.

5. Ann is Alice's _____.

6. Mary is Henry's _____.

7. Alan is Ann's _____.

8. Henry is Mary's _____.

9. Alice is Lisa's _____.

10. Henry is Ann's _____.

12 Physical characteristics

Complete the sentences. Choose one of the words in parentheses.

1. He is _thin_ .
   (fat/thin)

2. She has _____ hair.
   (blond/brown)

3. He has a _____ .
   (beard/mustache)

4. She has _____ hair.
   (black/blond)

5. He is _____ .
   (average height/tall)

6. She is _____ .
   (short/tall)

7. She has gray _____ .
   (eyes/hair)

8. He is _____ .
   (thin/average weight)

13 Food

A. Match the pictures and the words.

g   1. onion
___ 2. ice cream
___ 3. soda
___ 4. green pepper
___ 5. chicken
___ 6. apple
___ 7. egg
___ 8. cake
___ 9. carrot
___ 10. garlic

B. Put the foods from exercise 1 in the correct columns.

Vegetables	Fruit	Fish, Meat, Eggs
green pepper		

Desserts	Drinks	Bread, Rice, Spices

14 Ordinal numbers

A. Match the dates on the calendar with the dates in the column below.

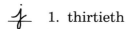 1. thirtieth

_____ 2. eighteenth

_____ 3. fifteenth

_____ 4. twenty-eighth

_____ 5. first

_____ 6. thirteenth

_____ 7. eleventh

_____ 8. thirty-first

_____ 9. eighth

_____ 10. fifth

January 1992						
Sunday	Monday	Tuesday	Wednesday	Thursday	Friday	Saturday
		1 ⓓ	2	3	4	5 ⓕ
6	7	8 ⓐ	9	10	11 ⓔ	12
13 ⓘ	14	15 ⓗ	16	17	18 ⓑ	19
20	21	22	23	24	25	26
27	28 ⓒ	29	30 ⓙ	31 ⓖ		

B. Write the correct numbers under the columns: 1st, 2nd, 3rd, . . . 10th.

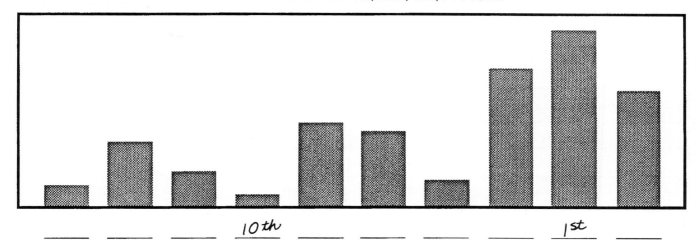

_____ _____ _____ _10th_ _____ _____ _____ _____ _1st_ _____

LESSON 1

EXERCISE 1

Complete this conversation. Use *'m (am)*, *'s (is)*, and *are*.

John: Hi. I _'m_ John. What _____ your name?
                    1   2

Teresa: My name _____ Rosa.
                          3

John: What _____ your last name?
                      4

Teresa: Hernandez.

John: Where _____ you from, Teresa?
                        5

Teresa: I _____ from California.
                  6

Where _____ you from?
            7

John: I _____ from New York.
                8

EXERCISE 2

The spelling of one word in each group is not correct. Circle it and write it correctly.

1. hi (helo) where what _____hello_____
2. Mexico China Spaine Puerto Rico _____
3. pleese thanks could from _____
4. practice spel use talk _____
5. conversation information exersize partner _____
6. alphabet name lesson contry _____

Rewrite the sentences in parentheses to make a dialogue. Use contractions.

1. **Carlos:** *Hi. My name's Carlos.* _____ (Hi. My name is Carlos.)

    _____ (I am from Colombia.)

    _____ (What is your name?)

 Lucy: _____ (I am Lucy.)

    _____ (I am from Mexico.)

2. **Mrs. Brennan:** _____ (What is your first name?)

 Pierre: _____ (My first name is Pierre.)

 Mrs. Brennan: _____ (What is your last name?)

 Pierre: _____ (My last name is Blanc.)

    _____ (I am from Canada.)

Answer the questions. Use your own information.

1. What's your name? _____

2. What's your first name? _____

3. What's your last name? _____

4. Where are you from? _____

EXERCISE 1

Fill in the blanks with *'m, 's, or 're.*

1. This is Oscar.

   He _'s_ from Spain.

2. This is Tetsuo and this is Keiko.

   They _____ from Japan.

3. This is Ann Brennan.

   She _____ from the United States.

4. I'm Lucy and this is Marco.

   We _____ from Mexico.

5. This is Pravit.

   He _____ from Thailand.

6. This is me.

   I _____ from _____ .

EXERCISE 2

Fill in the blanks with *What, Where,* or *How.*

1. A: _Where_ are you from?
   B: I'm from Mexico.

2. A: _____ is your name?
   B: Lynn.

3. A: _____ is she from?
   B: China.

4. A: _____ are you?
   B: Fine, thanks.

5. A: _____ 's her last name?
   B: Brennan.

6. A: _____ are you and Gina from?
   B: We're from Italy.

Put the words in the correct order.

1. A: you how are

   A: _How are you_ ?

   B: am fine I

   B: _____ .

   A: too I fine am

   A: _____ , _____ .

2. A: your name is what

   A: _____ ?

   B: Keiko name is my

   B: _____ .

   A: you where are from

   A: _____ ?

   B: Japan am from I

   B: _____ .

3. A: Tony Gina is this

   A: _____ , _____ .

   new a student is she

   _____ .

   B: meet to you nice

   B: _____ .

   C: too to meet nice you

   C: _____ , _____ .

Complete the conversation.

Keiko: Hello. _How are you_ ?
                              1

Marco: Fine, thanks. And you?

Keiko: Fine, thanks. _____ ?
                                    2

Marco: Marco Martinez.

Keiko: _____ ?
                    3

Marco: M-A-R-T-I-N-E-Z.

Keiko: _____ ?
                    4

Marco: Mexico. And this is Lucy.

Keiko: _____ ?
                    5

Marco: Lucy's from Mexico, too.

Keiko: _____ , Lucy.
                    6

Lucy: _____ , too.
                    7

EXERCISE 1

Read the conversation and circle the correct answers.

Good afternoon, Bob. How are you?

I'm fine thanks, Ted.

Hello, Bob. Nice to meet you, too.

Bob, this Amy Chan. She's a new teacher.

Hello, Amy. It's nice to meet you.

Ted Brooks   Bob Johnson   Amy Chan

1. a. Bob is a new teacher.
   b. Amy is a new teacher.

2. a. Ms. Chan's first name is Amy.
   b. Ms. Chan's first name is Bob.

3. a. Mr. Johnson's first name is Ted.
   b. Mr. Johnson's first name is Bob.

4. a. Bob's last name is Johnson.
   b. Bob's last name is Chan.

5. a. Ted Brooks's first name is Ted.
   b. Ted Brooks's last name is Ted.

EXERCISE 2

Circle the word or words that are different from the others on the line.

1. Goodbye.   Good night.   Hi.   See you tomorrow.
2. afternoon   hello   morning   evening
3. they   read   spell   listen
4. Mexico   Japan   English   China
5. am   what   is   are
6. where   what   how   thanks
7. it   is   he   she
8. Fine.   Hi.   Hello.   Good morning.

Complete the conversations. Use the words in the box.

This is Carlos.	Goodbye.
Fine, thanks. And you?	I'm from Thailand.
Nice to meet you, too.	How are you?
Where are you from?	I'm from Canada.

1. A: How are you?

   B: *Fine, thanks. And you?*

   A: I'm fine, too.

2. A: _____

   B: I'm from Spain. And you?

   A: _____

3. A: Hello.

   B: _____

   A: I'm fine.

4. A: _____

   B: I'm from Canada, too.

5. A: It's nice to meet you.

   B: _____

6. A: Lucy, _____

   B: Nice to meet you, Carlos.

7. A: _____

   B: See you tomorrow.

Circle the correct response.

1. Could you spell that, please?

   a. Nice to meet you.

   (b.) B-R-E-N-N-A-N.

2. Nice to meet you.

   a. Nice to meet you, too.

   b. Fine.

3. What's your first name?

   a. Ann Brennan.

   b. Ann.

4. How are you?

   a. You're fine.

   b. Fine, thanks.

5. Where are you from?

   a. I'm fine.

   b. China.

6. I'm fine, thanks. And you?

   a. I'm fine, too.

   b. It's nice.

7. What class are you in?

   a. The United States.

   b. English 203.

8. Goodbye.

   a. See you tomorrow.

   b. Fine.

LESSON 1

Complete the conversation. Use the words in the box and the information in the pictures.

| a/an | this/that | these/those | what | it | right |

Mrs. Brennan: What's ___*this*___ ?
1

Tetsuo: It's _____ English book.
2

Mrs. Brennan: No, _____ isn't an English book.
3

Carlos: It's _____ Spanish book.
4

Mrs. Brennan: Right. And _____ are _____ ?
5 6

Tetsuo: Those are _____ .
7

Mrs. Brennan: _____ .
8

Write a sentence about each picture. Use *this, that, these,* or *those.*

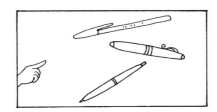

1. _What's that ?_

2. _____

3. _____

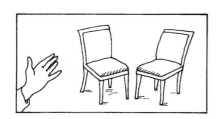

4. _____

5. _____

6. _____

Unscramble the words. Then write the word with *a* or *an*.

1. mubleral *an umbrella*

2. rasree _____

3. clkabdaorb _____

4. tawsetabkes _____

5. klocc _____

6. tipruec _____

7. shEnlig kobo _____

8. sinpaSh tendust _____

Write *That's right* or *That's wrong*. Correct the statements that are wrong.

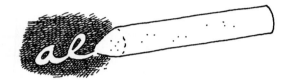

1. That's a pencil.

That's wrong. It's a piece of chalk.

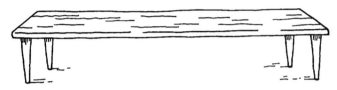

2. That's a desk.

_____

 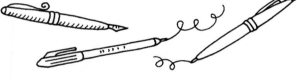

3. Those are pens.

4. That's a Chinese book.

_____

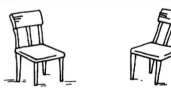

5. Those are chairs.

6. Those are handbags.

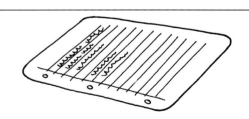

7. Those are pieces of paper.

8. That's a notebook.

_____

22   UNIT 2

EXERCISE 1

Complete the conversations.

1. A: Is this Room 381?

   B: <u>*No, it isn't.*</u>

   You're in the wrong room.

2. A: Is this Room 322?

   B: _____

   You're in the _____ room.

3. A: _____ ?

   B: Yes, it is.

   _____

4. A: _____ ?

   B: No, it isn't room 132.

   _____

5. A: _____ ?

   B: _____

   You're in the right room.

6. A: _____ ?

   B: _____

   _____

Complete the conversation.

Hiro: Hi. Are you __a__ new student?
            1

Rosa: Yes, I ____ . Are you?
              2

Hiro: ____ , I'm not. My name's Hiro.
          3

I'm _____ Japan.
        4

Rosa: Hi. _____ Rosa.
              5

Hiro: _____ you from Spain, Rosa?
              6

Rosa: No, I'm _____ . I'm from Mexico.
                  7

Hiro: ____ this English 101?
          8

Rosa: No, ____ isn't. It's English 102.
              9

Hiro: Oh. I'm in the _____ room!
                        10

Match the sentences on the left with the responses on the right.

1. Are you a student?   __d__

2. Is this English 201?   ____

3. Is your teacher from the United States?   ____

4. Are your classmates from China?   ____

5. Are you and your classmates in the right room?   ____

6. Am I late?   ____

a.   Yes, we are.

b.   No, you're not.

c.   Yes, they are.

d.   No, I'm not.

e.   Yes, it is.

f.   Yes, he (she) is.

Answer questions 1–5 in exercise 3. Use your own information.

1. _____

2. _____

3. _____

4. _____

5. _____

Read Terry Evan's registration card and complete the dialogue.

Registration Form

Evans	Terry
Last Name	First Name

1970	Sacramento, California
Year of Birth	Place of Birth

1078	Marine Drive
No.	Street

Dallas	Texas	75214
City	State	Zip Code

(214) 555-8790	Terry Evans
Area Code Telephone	Signature

Secretary: ¹ _What's your name ?_ _____

Terry: Terry Evans.

Secretary: ² _____

Terry: 1078 Marine Drive.

Secretary: ³ _____

Terry: (214) 555–8790

Secretary: ⁴ _____

Terry: Sacramento, California. 1970.

Secretary: ⁵ _____

Terry: You're welcome.

Read this page from a phone book.

	692-9860	Aguada ...		
	340-7157	Agudelo Alvaro & Damaris		
	440-1689	· 32 Elizabeth Mh · · · · · ·	592-7475	
	955-0630	Adams, John 24 Port Road........................555-6150		
	919-1560	Aldeson, Barbara 102 Lincoln Boulevard...555-1036		
	440 4914	Alvarez, Liz 6 School Avenue.......................555-8042		
		Andrews, Douglas 523 Water Street............555-7851		
	546-6112	Aston, David 1939 Blue Street.....................555-0317		
	652-5510	Barnes, Maria 809 North Road......................555-6688		
	664-8079	Bell, Thomas 257 California Road.................555-8934		
	666-1561	Agagliaro Joseph 97 Summit ... · 444-1529		
	465-7256	Açala Alfredo 256 ... · · 769-5449		
	652-5687	Aguiar Arelino 103 Slocum ... · 567-3907		

Check T (true) or F (false).

	T	F
1. John's last name is Adams.	T	
2. Mr. Andrew's first name is David.		
3. Ms. Barnes's address is 890 North Road.		
4. Thomas's phone number is 555–8934.		
5. Maria's phone number is 555–0317.		
6. Ms. Alvarez's address is 523 Water Street.		
7. David's last name is Aston.		

Match the words on the left with the information on the right.

1. name _d_   a. 555 –1454

2. zip code _____   b. Brenda

3. telephone number _____   c. 1985 Main Street

4. year of birth _____   d. Brenda Smith

5. course number _____   e. Spanish 207

6. address _____   f. Smith

7. place of birth _____   g. 1956

8. first name _____   h. Spain

9. signature _____   i. 19856

10. last name _____   j. *Brenda Smith*

EXERCISE 1

Match the words on the left with the words on the right.

1. brother ___f___   a. husband
2. mother _____   b. children
3. wife _____   c. married
4. son _____   d. dog
5. parents _____   e. father
6. grandfather _____   f. sister
7. cat _____   g. daughter
8. single _____   h. grandmother

EXERCISE 2

Fill in the blanks with *my, your, his, her, its, our,* or *their.*

This is Mary. This is ___her___ husband. _____ name is Jim. _____ daughter
                        1   2   3
is Molly. She's married. _____ husband is Bill. Molly and Bill have two children. _____
                          4   5
names are David and Ann. The children have a cat. _____ name is Tiger.
                                                    6

Look at Jane's family tree and complete the conversation.

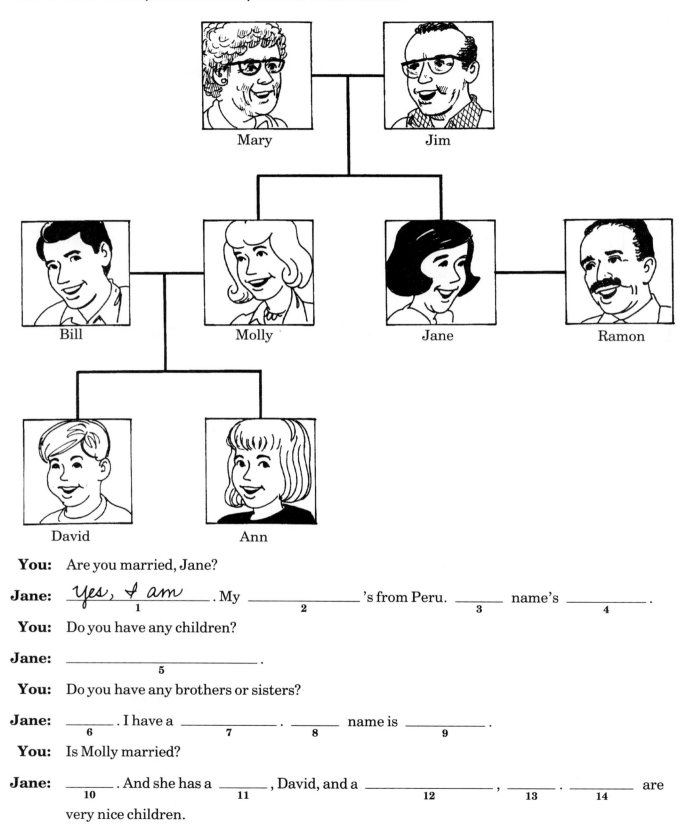

Mary   Jim

Bill   Molly   Jane   Ramon

David   Ann

You: Are you married, Jane?

Jane: _Yes, I am_ . My _____ 's from Peru. _____ name's _____ .
        1   2   3   4

You: Do you have any children?

Jane: _____ .
                    5

You: Do you have any brothers or sisters?

Jane: _____ . I have a _____ . _____ name is _____ .
          6   7   8   9

You: Is Molly married?

Jane: _____ . And she has a _____ , David, and a _____ , _____ . _____ are
          10   11   12   13   14
very nice children.

EXERCISE 1

Look at the pictures and complete the sentences.

1. _This is Gina's_____ ID card.

2. _____ notebooks.

3. _____ mother.

4. _____ address.

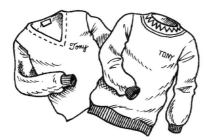

5. _____ sweaters.

6. _____ wallet.

EXERCISE 2

Write a question for each answer.

1. _Where's he from?_____

He's from China.

2. _____

They're from Japan.

3. _____

He's Canadian.

4. _____

She's a doctor.

5. _____

He's 42.

6. _____

We're American.

7. _____

He's a teacher.

8. _____

She's 17.

Fill in the blanks. Use the words in the box.

How	Who	a	Where
He	What	That's	from

A: _Who_ is that?
   ¹

B: _____ Oscar Garcia.
        ²

A: _____ 's he from?
        ³

B: He's _____ Spain.
              ⁴

A: _____ 's his occupation?
        ⁵

B: He's _____ doctor.
              ⁶

A: _____ old is he?
        ⁷

B: _____ 's 31.
        ⁸

Read the sentences and fill in the chart.

	Country	Nationality	Age	Occupation
Keiko				
Yon Mi				
Marco				
Lynn			21	photographer
Roberto				

1. Lynn is a photographer. She's 21.
2. Keiko is from Japan. She's Japanese.
3. Roberto is a reporter. He's Puerto Rican.
4. Yon Mi is Korean. She's a computer programmer.
5. Marco is 50. He's from Mexico.
6. Lynn is from China. She's Chinese.
7. Roberto is from Puerto Rico. He's 33.
8. Keiko is a secretary. She's 19.
9. Yon Mi is 25. She's from Korea.
10. Marco is Mexican. He's a security guard.

Describe the people in each picture.

tall
young
handsome
brown hair

short
glasses
mustache
black hair

1. Yon Mi's brother.

He's tall. He has brown hair.
He's young and handsome.

2. Marco's father

_____

_____

pretty
blue eyes
blond hair
average height

old
thin
not pretty
brown eyes

3. Gina's sister

_____

_____

_____

4. Lucy's cat

_____

_____

_____

Match the questions and the responses.

1. Is this your English book? _c_   a. Yes, I am.

2. What's your occupation? _____   b. Blond.

3. Are these your English exercises? _____   c. No, it isn't.

4. What nationality are you? _____   d. Yes. A daughter.

5. Are you married? _____   e. 21.

6. Where are you from? _____   f. Brown.

7. How old are you? _____   g. Japan.

8. What color is your hair? _____   h. I'm a carpenter.

9. What color are your eyes? _____   i. Japanese.

10. Do you have any children? _____   j. No, they aren't.

Now answer the questions in exercise 2. Use your own information.

1. _____

2. _____

3. _____

4. _____

5. _____

6. _____

7. _____

8. _____

9. _____

10. _____

EXERCISE 1

Complete the letter. Use 's (is) and are.

> Dear Mom and Dad
>
> I have a new apartment in Dallas. There **are** five rooms in my apartment. There____ a living room. There____ a kitchen. There____ a bathroom. And there ____ two bedrooms.
>
> The living room ____ beautiful. There ____ four windows in the room. There____ a big sofa. There ____ two small chairs. There ____ two tables, two lamps, and a television. There____ a rug on the floor, and there____ some pictures on the walls.

EXERCISE 2

Write a (an) or the in the blanks.

This is ___a___ bathroom in _____ old house. _____ bathroom is small. There is _____
          1   2   3   4
sink in _____ bathroom. There is _____ bathtub in the bathroom. There is _____ toilet
          5   6   7
in _____ bathroom. There is _____ window in the bathroom, too. _____ bathtub is under
      8   9   10
_____ window.
  11

Look at the picture. Then choose the correct prepositions.

1. There's a bed _____*in*_____ the bedroom. (in/next to)

2. There's a cat _____ the bed. (under/on)

3. There's a desk _____ the door. (next to/in front of)

4. There are two pictures _____ the desk. (over/on)

5. There's a clock _____ the desk. (in/on)

6. There's a wastebasket _____ the desk. (next to/behind)

7. There's a lamp _____ the bed. (behind/in front of)

8. There's a rug _____ the desk and the bed. (next to/between)

Look at the pictures in exercise 3. Write sentences with *some*.

1. _There are some lamps in the room._

2. _____

3. _____

4. _____

EXERCISE 1

Write five sentences about this room. Use *There is* (*There's*) and *There are*. Also use *in, on, around, under, over, between,* or *next to.*

1. <u>There's a clock over the refrigerator.</u>
2. _____
3. _____
4. _____
5. _____

EXERCISE 2

Look at the picture in exercise 1. Then look at this picture. Write five sentences about what is different.

1. <u>There aren't any curtains on the window.</u>
2. _____
3. _____
4. _____
5. _____

Answer the questions about the picture.

1. Is there a teacher in the classroom? _No, there isn't._

2. Are there any windows? _____

3. Is there a blackboard? _____

4. Are there any students? _____

Now write your own questions and answers.

5. A: (umbrella) _Is there an umbrella in the classroom ?_

   B: _____

6. A: (curtains) _____

   B: _____

7. A: (clock) _____

   B: _____

8. A: (erasers) _____

   B: _____

Answer these questions about the picture in exercise 3.

1. How many windows are there? _There are two._

2. How many desks are there? _____

3. How many books are there? _____

4. How many clocks are there? _____

EXERCISE 1

Fill in the blanks with the correct number.

1. Sunday is the _first_ day of the week.

2. Monday is the _____ day of the week.

3. Tuesday is the _____ day of the week.

4. Wednesday is the _____ day of the week.

5. Thursday is the _____ day of the week.

6. Friday is the _____ day of the week.

7. Saturday is the _____ day of the week.

January 1992						
Sunday	Monday	Tuesday	Wednesday	Thursday	Friday	Saturday
			1	2	3	4
5	6	7	8	9	10	11
12	13	14	15	16	17	18
19	20	21	22	23	24	25
26	27	28	29	30	31	

EXERCISE 2

Look at the calendars and write the dates.

Jan. 1990

S	M	T	W	T	F	S
	1	2	3	4	5	6
7	8	9	10	11	12	13
14	15	16	17	18	19	20
21	22	23	24	25	26	27
28	29	30	31			

1. _It's January 8, 1990._

Dec. 1991

S	M	T	W	T	F	S
1	2	3	4	5	6	7
8	9	10	11	12	13	14
15	16	17	18	19	20	21
22	23	24	25	26	27	28
29	30	31				

2. _____

Apr. 1994

S	M	T	W	T	F	S
					1	2
3	4	5	6	7	8	9
10	11	12	13	14	15	16
17	18	19	20	21	22	23
24	25	26	27	28	29	30

3. _____

Sept. 1992

S	M	T	W	T	F	S
		1	2	3	4	5
6	7	8	9	10	11	12
13	14	15	16	17	18	19
20	21	22	23	24	25	26
27	28	29	30	31		

4. _____

Jul. 1993

S	M	T	W	T	F	S
				1	2	3
4	5	6	7	8	9	10
11	12	13	14	15	16	17
18	19	20	21	22	23	24
25	26	27	28	29	30	31

5. _____

TODAY?

6. _____

Choose the correct word.

1. There are ___*sixteen*___ students in the class. (sixteen/sixteenth)

2. Keiko's birthday is December _____ . (two/second)

3. The _____ month of the year is January. (one/first)

4. February has _____ days. (twenty-eight/twenty-eighth)

5. There are _____ chairs in Lynn's kitchen. (three/third)

6. This is Unit _____ . (Four/Fourth)

7. Today is February _____ . (fourteen/fourteenth)

8. There are _____ months in a year. (twelve/twelfth)

9. December is the _____ month of the year. (twelve/twelfth)

10. This is number _____ . (ten/tenth)

Describe each picture. Use the words in the box.

| rainy and cool | cold and snowy |
| hot and sunny | windy and cloudy |

1. _It's cold and snowy._

2. _____

3. _____

4. _____

EXERCISE 1

Look at the picture and read the sentences. Then write *That's right* or *That's wrong*. Correct the sentences that are wrong.

1. John is working at the library today.

   That's wrong. He is working at the restaurant.

2. Anna is reading the newspaper.

   _____

   _____

3. Dr. Green is relaxing today.

   _____

   _____

4. Mr. and Mrs. Wong aren't working today.

   _____

   _____

YOU

5. Hiro isn't watching TV.

   _____

   _____

6. I'm reading the newspaper.

   _____

   _____

Look at the pictures in exercise 1. Then write questions and short answers.

1. John/work/home?

   A: *Is John working at home?*

   B: *No, he isn't.*

2. Anna/read/newspaper?

   A: _____

   B: _____

3. Dr. Green/relax?

   A: _____

   B: _____

4. Mr. and Mrs. Wong/relax?

   A: _____

   B: _____

5. Hiro/clean/kitchen?

   A: _____

   B: _____

6. you/talk/on the phone?

   A: _____

   B: _____

Complete the telephone conversation.

A: Hi, Molly. Are you busy?

B: I *'m reading* _____ the newspaper, and David and Ann _____
   1 read   2 watch

   television. What about you? _____ you _____ today?
                               3   work

A: No, I _____ . I _____ at home. Bill _____ a
         4   5 relax   6 visit

   friend in New York.

B: Oh, ____ he _____ in a hotel?
       7   stay

A: Yes, he ____ . And he _____ at some very nice restaurants!
           8   9 eat

B: Oh, my sister _____ at the door. Speak to you later!
                 10 knock

A: OK. Bye.

What are they doing? Complete the questions. Then answer them.

1. What **'s** Dr. Green *doing*_____?
She's talking to her husband.
talk to her husband

2. _____ John doing?
_____
study

3. What _____ Mary and Jim _____?
_____
visit friends in Montana

4. _____ Anna _____?
_____
work

5. _____ Hiro _____?
_____
shop

6. _____ Molly _____?
_____
take pictures

7. _____ Mrs. Wong _____?
_____
read the newspaper

YOU

8. What are YOU doing?
_____

Choose the correct sentence ending.

1. Grapes are _b_ .

   a. yellow.

   b. purple.

2. The sun is ____ .

   a. black.

   b. yellow.

3. Tomatoes are ____ .

   a. red.

   b. gray.

4. Lettuce is ____ .

   a. pink.

   b. green.

5. Snow is ____ .

   a. white.

   b. brown.

6. Carrots are ____ .

   a. orange.

   b. blue.

Unscramble the words. Then write the plural forms.

1. ath   _hat_   _hats_

2. selbou   _____   _____

3. thcaw   _____   _____

4. cenkclae   _____   _____

5. tius   _____   _____

6. fracs   _____   _____

7. strik   _____   _____

8. ite   _____   _____

9. crabetel   _____   _____

10. sreds   _____   _____

What are you wearing? Use colors in your answers.

_____

_____

_____

_____

_____

EXERCISE 1

Read this FOR RENT ad and answer the questions.

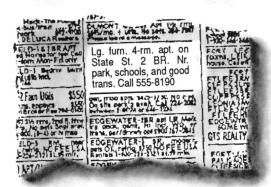

1. Is the apartment large or small?

   It's large.

2. Where is it?

   _____

3. How many rooms are there?

   _____

4. How many bedrooms are there?

   _____

5. Are there beds in the apartment?

   _____

6. What is the apartment near?

   _____

   _____

EXERCISE 2

Complete this description of the apartment for rent.

It's a _l a r g e_ f _ _ _ _ - r _ _ _ _ a _ _ _ _ _ _ _ _ _ _ on State S _ _ _ _ _ _.

It is f _ _ _ _ _ _ _ _ _ _. It has t _ _ b _ _ _ _ _ _ _ _ _. It is n _ _ _ _ the park,

schools, and good t _ _ _ _ _ _ _ _ _ _ _ _ _ _ _ _.

Write the names of the places in the correct locations.

1. The library is between the supermarket and the bank.
2. The hospital is across from the library on Walnut Street.
3. The post office is on the corner of Elm Street and Midway Avenue, across from the bank.
4. The restaurant is next to the post office.
5. The garage is on the corner of Elm Street and Midway Avenue, across from the post office.
6. The police station is next to the restaurant, across from the supermarket

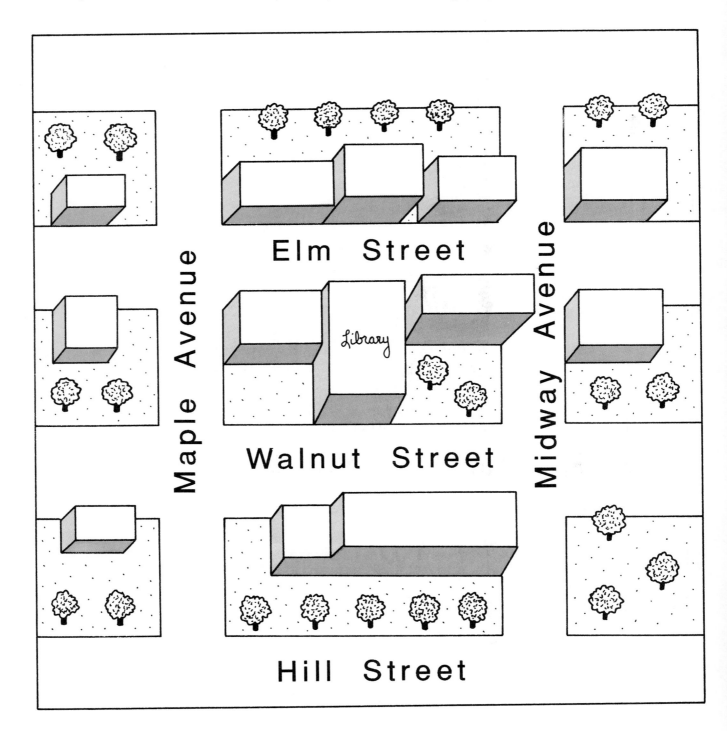

Complete the conversations. Use the information in exercise 3.

1. A: Where's the police station?

   B: It's _next_ _to_ the restaurant.

   It's ____ _____ _____ ____ Maple Avenue and Elm Street.

2. A: _____ me. _____ ____ the hotel?

   B: It's _____ _____ the hospital.

3. A: Is there a bank in the neighborhood?

   B: Yes, it's _____ to the _____ .

4. A: Excuse me. Is the post office next to the library?

   B: ____ , ____ _____ .

EXERCISE 1

Use the words to make sentences.

1. Sunday   do   errands   on   they

   They do errands on Sunday.

2. play   tennis   every day   they

   _____

3. children   go   Ann and Jerry's   to school   in the morning

   _____

4. to the movies   after dinner   they   go

   _____

5. go   I   swimming   Saturday   on

   _____

6. to Friday   in a hospital   work   they   from Monday

   _____

EXERCISE 2

Complete with the days of the week.

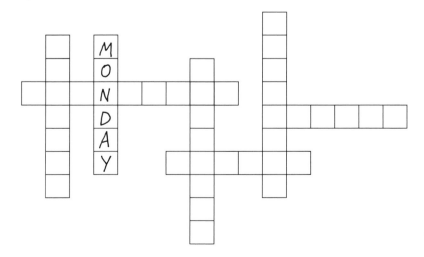

Look at the class schedule. Then complete the paragraph.

Monday	Tuesday	Wednesday	Thursday	Friday	Saturday
English	math	English	math	English	
history	science	history	science	history	
math	English	math	English	math	
lunch	*lunch*	*lunch*	*lunch*	*lunch*	
science	French	music	music	science	
French	tennis	French	history	swimming	

Jeff and Lois are students. They _go_ to school on Monday, Tuesday, Wednesday,
1

_____ , and Friday. They _____ go to school on Saturday.
2   3

Jeff and Lois _____ English. They have English every _____ . They _____ French, too.
4   5   6

They _____ French on Monday, Tuesday, and _____ . They
7   8

_____ French on Thursday and Friday. On Friday they have _____
9   10

after lunch. _____ science they go swimming.
11

Jeff and Lois _____ history on Monday, _____ , Thursday, and Friday. They
12   13

_____ history on Tuesday.
14

Complete the conversation. Use the information from the schedule in exercise 3.

A: ¹ *Do they have English?* _____

B: Yes, they have English every day.

A: ² _____ , too?

B: Yes. They have French on Monday, Tuesday, and Wednesday.

A: Do they study Spanish?

B: ³ _____

A: Do they go to school ⁴ _____ Saturday?

B: ⁵ _____

A: Do they have history on Monday?

B: ⁶ _____

A: ⁷ _____ lunch in school?

B: Yes, they do.

Read this paragraph from Keiko's letter.

> I'm very busy these days. From Monday to Friday, I get up
> early and exercise. Then I take a shower and eat
> breakfast. After breakfast, I go to work. I work all
> morning at the office. Then I eat lunch. After lunch, I
> study. Then I eat dinner and go to class with Lynn. After
> class, we watch television. I go to bed very late. I'm
> busy, but I'm happy.

Now rewrite the paragraph. Change *I* to *she* and *we* to *they*.

She's very busy these days.

Look at Oscar's list of daily activities. Then complete the conversation.

A: What's Oscar like?

B: Oh, he is very serious about his work and school. He has a very busy schedule.

A: _Does_ he _____ up early every day?
   ₁   ₂

B: _____, he does.
   ₃

A: _____ he exercise?
   ₄

B: Yes, he _____ in the park.
         ₅

A: _____ he _____ lunch in the cafeteria?
   ₆   ₇

B: No, he _____. He _____ lunch
            ₈   ₉
   in his office.

A: _____ he ____ to class before or after work?
   ₁₀   ₁₁

B: He _____ to class after work.
       ₁₂

A: _____ he relax after class?
   ₁₃

B: Yes, he _____. After class he _____ home.
           ₁₄   ₁₅
   He _____ dinner. He _____ TV, and then
       ₁₆   ₁₇
   he _____ to bed.
       ₁₈

Oscar's daily activities

get up early
jog in park
take shower and get dressed
eat breakfast
go to work
go to class
go home
eat dinner
watch TV
go to bed

Match the questions and answers.

1. Does Keiko work?   _e_   a. No, he doesn't.

2. Do Oscar and Alicia play tennis? ____   b. She's serious.

3. What's Alicia like? ____   c. No, they aren't.

4. Does Felix have a job? ____   d. Yes, they do.

5. Are Oscar and Alicia lazy? ____ e. Yes, she does.

6. Do you have any brothers or sisters? ____   f. Yes, she is.

7. Is Keiko happy? ____   g. No, I don't.

This is a letter from Felix's young cousin Carla. There are eight (8) mistakes in the letter. Find and correct the mistakes.

> Dear Felix,
>
> How are you? Are you busy? Do you ~~working~~ *work* all day?
> How is Alicia and Oscar? Does Alicia lives near you?
> I'm very happy. I go to school from Monday to Friday. I
> go not on Saturday and Sunday. And I am speaking English
> every day at school. After school I play with my friend
> Rosalie. She have two sisters and a brother. Sometimes we
> are playing baseball in the park.
>
> How is your new girlfriend? What's she likes? Write
> to me soon.
>
> Love,
> Carla

Circle the correct response.

1. Spell your last name please.

   a. Yes.

   b. S-m-i-t-h.

2. What's your occupation?

   a. I teach math.

   b. I am very busy.

3. Do you have any brothers or sisters?

   a. Frank and Laura.

   b. One brother and one sister.

4. Do your sisters live near you?

   a. Yes, she does.

   b. Yes, they do.

5. What's your sister like?

   a. Very serious.

   b. Her job.

6. Do you work on the weekend?

   a. Yes, I work on Saturday and Sunday.

   b. No, I work on Saturday and Sunday.

A friend or relative is visiting you. Write a letter about this person. Answer some of these questions.

What's his/her name?
Where is he/she from?
What's his/her occupation?
What are you and your friend/relative doing now?

_____

_____

_____

_____

_____

_____

_____

_____

_____

_____

_____

_____

Which word doesn't belong? Cross it out.

1. Saturday   Monday   Sunday   ~~Tony~~

2. history   science   job   math

3. weekend   before   after   when

4. breakfast   dish   lunch   dinner

5. think   wash   plays   like

6. going   working   eat   staying

7. near   on   but   at

8. don't   isn't   could   doesn't

EXERCISE 1

Look at the pictures. Then rewrite these sentences correctly.

1. Mr. and Mrs. Wong get up at 8:00.

Mr. and Mrs. Wong don't get up
at 8:00. They get up at 6:00.

2. Mr. Wong eats breakfast at 7:15.

_____

_____

3. They arrive at work at 8:00.

_____

_____

4. Mr. and Mrs. Wong eat lunch at 1:15.

_____

_____

5. Mr. Wong leaves work at 9:00.

_____

_____

6. Mrs. Wong eats dinner at 6:00.

_____

_____

Two students are talking about their schedules. Complete their conversation.

A: When *do you have breakfast* ?

B: I have breakfast at 7:30.

A: What time _____ ?

B: I leave for school at 9:15.

A: How _____ ?

B: I go to school by bus.

A: Where _____ ?

B: I eat lunch in the park.

A: And when _____ ?

B: I finish dinner at 8:00.

Answer these questions.

1. When do you get up?

   _____

2. What time do you leave for school (or work)?

   _____

3. How do you go to school (or work)?

   _____

4. Where do you eat lunch?

   _____

5. What time do you finish class (or work)?

   _____

6. How do you get home from school (or work)?

   _____

Read the schedule and complete the conversation.

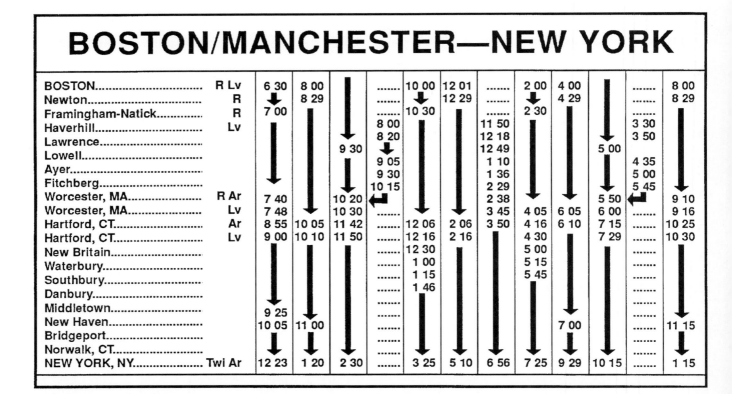

BOSTON.................... R Lv	6 30	8 00		....	10 00	12 01	....	2 00	4 00		....	8 00
Newton..................... R	↓	8 29		....	↓	12 29	....	↓	4 29		....	8 29
Framingham-Natick....... R	7 00			....	10 30		....	2 30			....	
Haverhill.................. Lv				8 00			11 50				3 30	
Lawrence..................			↓	8 20			12 18			5 00	3 50	
Lowell....................			9 30	↓			12 49				4 35	
Ayer......................				9 05			1 10				5 00	
Fitchberg.................				9 30			1 36				5 45	
Worcester, MA.......... R Ar	7 40		10 20 ←	10 15			2 29		5 50	←		9 10
Worcester, MA............ Lv	7 48		10 30				2 38		6 00			9 16
Hartford, CT.............. Ar	8 55	10 05	11 42	....	12 06	2 06	3 45	4 05	6 05		....	10 25
Hartford, CT.............. Lv	9 00	10 10	11 50	....	12 16	2 16	3 50	4 16	6 10	7 15	....	10 30
New Britain...............				....	12 30		4 30	5 00		7 29	....	
Waterbury.................				....	1 00			5 15			....	
Southbury.................				....	1 15			5 45			....	
Danbury...................				....	1 46						....	
Middletown................	9 25			....					7 00		....	
New Haven.................	10 05	11 00		....							....	11 15
Bridgeport................	↓	↓		....					↓		....	↓
Norwalk, CT..............			↓	....							....	
NEW YORK, NY........... Twi Ar	12 23	1 20	2 30	....	3 25	5 10	6 56	7 25	9 29	10 15	....	1 15

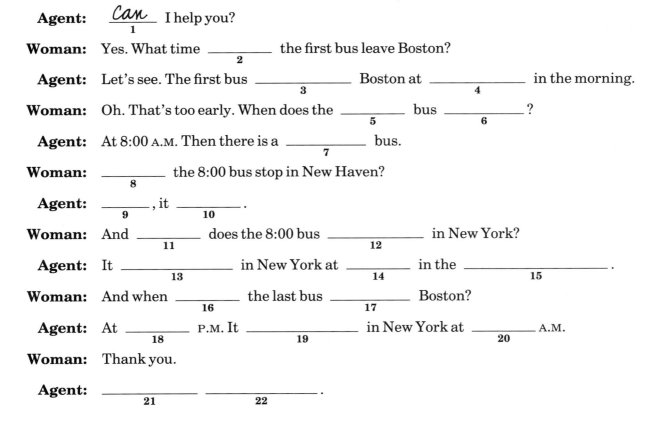

Agent: _Can_ I help you?
   ‾‾‾‾1

Woman: Yes. What time _____ the first bus leave Boston?
                              2

Agent: Let's see. The first bus _____ Boston at _____ in the morning.
                                      3   4

Woman: Oh. That's too early. When does the _____ bus _____ ?
                                               5   6

Agent: At 8:00 A.M. Then there is a _____ bus.
                                         7

Woman: _____ the 8:00 bus stop in New Haven?
            8

Agent: _____ , it _____ .
            9   10

Woman: And _____ does the 8:00 bus _____ in New York?
                11   12

Agent: It _____ in New York at _____ in the _____ .
              13   14   15

Woman: And when _____ the last bus _____ Boston?
                    16   17

Agent: At _____ P.M. It _____ in New York at _____ A.M.
              18   19   20

Woman: Thank you.

Agent: _____ _____ .
            21   22

EXERCISE 1

Find the sentences that match.

1. Marco likes westerns. _d_
2. Lucy doesn't like cats. ____
3. Tony doesn't eat Mexican food. ____
4. Gina takes the bus to work. ____
5. Ann and Jerry shop on Friday. ____
6. Olga and Hector don't jog. ____

a. I shop on Friday.
b. Lynn and Keiko don't jog.
c. Pravit takes the bus to work.
d. Carlos likes westerns.
e. Tetsuo doesn't eat Mexican food.
f. Simon doesn't like cats.

Now combine the sentences with *and*. Use *too* or *either*.

1. _Marco like westerns, and Carlos likes westerns, too._
2. _____
   _____
3. _____
   _____
4. _____
   _____
5. _____
6. _____
   _____

EXERCISE 2

What about you? Make true sentences about the people in exercise 1 and yourself.
Use *too, either, but,* or *and*.

1. Marco _likes westerns, and I do, too._

2. Tetsuo _____

3. Olga and Hector _____

4. Pravit _____

5. Lucy _____

6. Ann and Jerry _____

Unscramble the words. Then check the correct column or columns.

			Adjective	Adverb
1.	fulraceyl	*carefully*	☐	☑
2.	rahd		☐	☐
3.	adb		☐	☐
4.	lewl		☐	☐
5.	telyan		☐	☐
6.	tafs		☐	☐
7.	woslyl		☐	☐
8.	teauiblufyl		☐	☐
9.	odog		☐	☐
10.	wols		☐	☐

Look at the information about Lynn and Keiko. Then complete the paragraph.

	Lynn	Keiko
good dancer	yes	no
fast swimmer	no	yes
beautiful singer	no	no
neat writer	yes	yes
careful driver	no	yes
hard worker	yes	yes
good cook	yes	no

Keiko and Lynn are friends, but they are very different. Lynn dances very __well__ , but Keiko ____2____ . Keiko swims ____3____ , but Lynn swims ____4____ . Lynn doesn't drive very ____5____ , but Keiko ____6____ . Lynn cooks ____7____ , but Keiko is not a ____8____ cook. In some ways the two friends are the same. For example, Keiko and Lynn write ____9____ , and they are very ____10____ workers. The two women like music very much, but Lynn does not ____11____ well, and Keiko doesn't ____12____ .

EXERCISE 1

Complete these questions. Use *How, What, When,* or *Where.*

1. <u>*What*</u> time do you get up?

2. _____ do you eat breakfast?

3. I walk to school. _____ do you go to school?

4. _____ do you do when you get home from school?

5. _____ kind of movies do you like?

6. _____ do you go to bed?

EXERCISE 2

Answer the questions in exercise 1. Use your own information.

1. _____

2. _____

3. _____

4. _____

5. _____

6. _____

EXERCISE 3

Look at Gina's schedule. Then complete the paragraphs with *after, before, when, until,* and *from . . . until.*

My Schedule

7:30 *get up*
8:00 *jog*
8:30 *have breakfast*
9:00 *arrive at work*
12:00 *have lunch*
5:00 *leave work*
6:00 *have dinner*
7:00 *go to class*
8:30 *arrive home and study*
11:00 *go to bed*

Every day is a busy day for Gina. Gina's a bookkeeper. <u>*Before*</u>₁ she goes to work, she jogs and has breakfast. Then she works _____₂ 9:00 _____₃ 12:00. At 12:00 she eats lunch. _____₄ she has lunch, she works _____₅ 5:00, _____₆ she leaves work.

Gina is also a student. She goes to class five days a week. _____₇ she goes to class, she has dinner. _____₈ she arrives home, she studies _____₉ 8:30 _____₁₀ 11:00. Gina's days are long and hard.

Complete your schedule. Then, on a separate piece of paper, write about your day. Use *after*, *before*, *when*, *then*, and *from . . . until*. Remember to use commas (,).

My Schedule

6:00	_____	4:00	_____
7:00	_____	5:00	_____
8:00	_____	6:00	_____
9:00	_____	7:00	_____
10:00	_____	8:00	_____
11:00	_____	9:00	_____
12:00	_____	10:00	_____
1:00	_____	11:00	_____
2:00	_____	12:00	_____
3:00	_____	1:00	_____

Read the movie ad and answer the questions.

The Town Theater

TELL ME ABOUT IT!

A new comedy starting tonight!
Time: 5:00   7:00   9:00

1. What's playing tonight?

   Tell Me About It !

2. Where is it playing?

   _____

3. What kind of movie is it?

   _____

4. What time is the first show?

   _____

5. What time is the last show?

   _____

6. What other time is the movie playing?

   _____

58   UNIT 7

LESSON 1

EXERCISE 1

Put the following adverbs of frequency in order.

sometimes   seldom   often   usually   never   always

never   _____   _____   _____   _____   _____

EXERCISE 2

Use the words in exercise 1 to complete the interview with actor Rod Saxton, star of
Dead Men Don't Talk.

never _____ always

| go to a restaurant | have dinner with friends | watch TV | work late | jog before work | get up early |

Interviewer: How often do you get up early?

Rod: ¹ *I always get up early.* _____

Interviewer: I know you exercise. Do you ever jog before work?

Rod: ² _____

Interviewer: Do you ever work late?

Rod: ³ _____

Interviewer: You are very busy. Do you ever have dinner with friends?

Rod: ⁴ _____

Interviewer: How often do you go to a restaurant?

Rod: ⁵ _____

Interviewer: Do you ⁶ _____ relax? For example, do you ever watch TV?

Rod: Yes. ⁷ _____

Interviewer: Well, Mr. Saxton, thank you very much.

Rod: You're welcome.

What about you? How often do you do these things? Use *never, seldom, sometimes, often, usually,* or *always* in your answers.

1. (write letters) _____

2. (go to the movies) _____

3. (exercise) _____

4. (clean the house) _____

5. (be tired) _____

6. (cook) _____

7. (be on time) _____

8. (make mistakes) _____

Read about Jose. Complete the sentences with the correct form of the verbs.

Jose Garcia is a doctor. He

_____*works*_____ very hard.
      1 work

He usually _____
                        2 go
to the hospital, but today he

_____ . He
         3 work

_____ at home. He
         4 relax

seldom _____ TV,
              5 watch

but right now he _____
                          6 watch

a movie. He _____
                    7 enjoy

his day off. He _____
                          8 think

about his job at the hospital. Jose

_____ his work. He
         9 enjoy

is a very good doctor and always

_____ his job well.
         10 do

EXERCISE 1

Pierre is looking for a new job as a waiter. Look at the list of things a waiter or waitress has to do. Put the list in the correct order.

List of things a waiter or waitress has to do

_____ give the customers the check

_____ give the customers the food

_____ say hello to the customers

_____ say goodbye to the customers

_____ give the customers the menu

①_____ get to work on time

EXERCISE 2

Use the list in exercise 1 and write about Pierre's job. Use *has to*.

1. _He has to get to work on time._

2. _____

3. _____

4. _____

5. _____

6. _____

EXERCISE 3

Sally is a mechanic. Look at the picture. Write sentences about what she has to do and what she doesn't have to do at the garage. Use the words in the box.

wash the cars	work hard
fix the cars	speak to the customers
wear a suit	

1. _She doesn't have to wash the cars._

2. _____

3. _____

4. _____

5. _____

Lee is a secretary. What does he have to do? What doesn't he have to do?

answer the telephone	make copies
type letters	clean the office
make coffee	

1. _He has to answer the phone._

2. _____

3. _____

4. _____

5. _____

You are talking to Roberto about his job as a reporter. Complete the conversation with the correct form of *have to*.

You: Tell me about your job. What ¹ _do_ you _have to_ do?

Roberto: Oh, I ² _____ talk to people and ask them a lot of questions.

You: ³ ____ you _____ go to the office every day?

Roberto: No, I don't. A reporter often ⁴ _____ go to people's homes or to their offices.

You: Oh, I see. What ⁵ ____ you _____ wear?

Roberto: I can often wear blue jeans and a shirt. I ⁶ _____ always _____ wear a

suit and tie. I like that about my job.

You: ⁷ ____ you ever _____ get up very early?

Roberto: Yes, I do. But that's OK, because my job is always interesting.

Complete the dialogues by making suggestions with the words or phrases in parentheses.

1. A: I'm hungry.

   B: I'm hungry, too.

   Let's eat.
   _____
   eat

2. A: Are you tired?

   B: Yes, I am.

   _____
   go jogging

3. A: I'm bored.

   _____
   buy some good books

   B: Good idea. Where's the bookstore?

4. A: I'm sad.

   B: I'm sad, too.

   _____
   see *That's a Laugh!*

5. A: I'm lonely.

   B: I'm lonely, too.

   _____
   visit our friends

6. A: Are you nervous?

   B: Yes, I am.

   A: I'm nervous, too.

   _____
   go relax

It's 8:30 A.M. Lucy is on the phone with her friend Dana. Look at Lucy's schedule and complete the conversation. Use *Let's, have to, can't,* and the information in the schedule.

Dana: It's a beautiful morning. __*Let's*__ go for a walk.
                                            1

Lucy: I _____ . I _____ clean the house.
                2   3

Dana: Oh. Well, what about later? At 10:00?

Lucy: I really _____ . I have to _____ .
                      4   5

Dana: Well, what about lunch, then?

Lucy: I'm sorry. At 11:00 I _____ .
                                        6

Dana: And after work? _____ have dinner!
                              7

Lucy: I _____ see you then, either. I _____
             8   9
meet Simon, and after dinner I _____ study.
                                    10
Are you busy tomorrow?

Dana: No.

Lucy: Good! _____ have dinner then.
                    11

Dana: Great! See you tomorrow.

Things to Do Today

9:00 clean house

10:00 do errands

11:00 go to hospital

7:00 have dinner with Simon

9:00 study English

Lynn wrote a note to Keiko. The note is in code. Each number is a letter. For example, 1 = K, 2 = L. Can you read the note?

K   K
1 5 8 1 3,

        L
    2 5 11 9   5 6 11   2 13 10 15 12
                          L

11 3 4 5 11 12 5 14.

             L
9 5 5   7 3 13   2 6 11 5 14.

                       L
                   2 7 10 10

LESSON
1

EXERCISE 1

There are ten kinds of food hidden below. Can you find them?

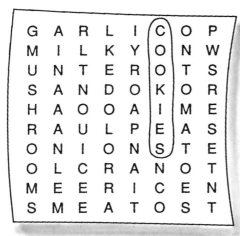

G	A	R	L	I	C	O	P
M	I	L	K	Y	O	N	W
U	N	T	E	R	O	T	S
S	A	N	D	O	K	O	R
H	A	O	O	A	I	M	E
R	A	U	L	P	E	A	S
O	N	I	O	N	S	T	E
O	L	C	R	A	N	O	N
M	E	E	R	I	C	E	T
S	M	E	A	T	O	S	T

EXERCISE 2

Write the foods from exercise 1 in the correct columns.

Things you can count
1. *cookies*
2.
3.
4.
5.

Things you can't count
6.
7.
8.
9.
10.

EXERCISE 3

Label the pictures. Use *a*, *an*, or *some*.

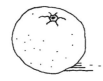

1. *an orange*

2. _____

3. _____

4. _____

5. _____

6. _____

7. _____

8. _____

9. _____

Look at the picture. Complete the dialogs with *some* or *any*.

1. A: _Is there any_ _____ tomato juice?

   B: _No, there isn't any tomato juice, but there is some_ _____

   orange juice. _____

2. A: _____ rice?

   B: _____

   _____

3. A: _____ green peppers?

   B: _____

   _____

4. A: _____ meat?

   B: _____

   _____

5. A: _____ coffee?

   B: _____

   _____

6. A: _____ onions?

   B: _____

   _____

Look at the picture below. Complete the conversation with *much, many, any,* or *a lot of*.

Keiko: How ___*many*___ potatoes do we have?
1

Lynn: We have _____ potatoes.
2

Keiko: And what about coffee? How _____ do we have?
3

Lynn: We don't have _____ coffee, but we have _____ tea.
4   5

Keiko: Are there _____ tomatoes?
6

Lynn: Yes, there are _____ tomatoes, and there is _____ rice, too.
7   8

Keiko: And how _____ oil do we have?
9

Lynn: We have _____ oil.
10

Keiko: Is there _____ milk?
11

Lynn: No, there isn't _____ milk. We need _____ things.
12   13

Write the prices next to the words below. Look at the price tags for help.

1. a dollar fifty-eight $ 1.58

2. a dollar ninety _____

3. ninety-nine cents _____

4. a dollar nineteen _____

5. a dollar nine _____

6. nineteen dollars and nineteen cents _____

7. sixty-nine cents _____

8. a dollar eighty-five _____

9. two seventy-nine _____

10. eighty-seven cents _____

Look at Roberto's shopping list. Complete the questions and answer them.

1. A: _How much_ bread does he need?

   B: _____

2. A: _____ apples _____?

   B: _____

3. A: _____ oranges _____?

   B: _____

4. A: _____?

   B: _____ a quart of _____.

5. A: _____?

   B: _____ a pound of _____.

6. A: _____.

   B: _____ a dozen (twelve) _____

2 loaves of bread
6 apples
1 pound coffee
1 dozen eggs
8 oranges
1 quart milk

Read the newspaper ad. Write questions and answers about the prices.

BUTTER	$1.69
	1 POUND
APPLE JUICE	$1.10
	1 QUART

ORANGES 1 POUND 39¢	EGGS
TOMATOES 1 POUND 48¢	98¢
LETTUCE HEAD 29¢	DOZEN

POTATOES
BAG 98¢

YOU *Save at Sam's*

CARROTS
A BUNCH
29¢

1. A: *How much are the tomatoes?*

   B: _____

2. A: _____

   B: _____

3. A: _____

   B: _____

4. A: _____

   B: _____

5. A: _____

   B: _____

6. A: _____

   B: _____

7. A: _____

   B: _____

One item in each group doesn't belong. Cross it out.

1. **a can of . . .** | soup   coffee   ~~lettuce~~   beans

2. **a pound of . . .** | tomatoes   rice   milk   chicken

3. **a bottle of . . .** | oil   juice   butter   milk

4. **a box of . . .** | jam   cookies   rice   candy

5. **a dozen . . .** | eggs   green peppers   cookies   butter

6. **a quart of . . .** | water   milk   sugar   juice

7. **a bag of . . .** | potatoes   tomatoes   onions   soup

EXERCISE 1

Read Ann Brennan's recipe for yellow cake.
Complete the directions for baking the cake.
Use the words in the box.

```
Vanilla Cake

1 cup butter          2½ cups flour
2 cups sugar          ½ teaspoon salt
4 eggs                1 teaspoon
2 teaspoons             baking powder
  vanilla extract     1 cup milk
```

add	bake	cool	heat
mix	put	stir	

Heat the oven to 350 degrees. _____ the sugar, butter, and eggs in a bowl. _____ well.
    1   2   3

_____ the vanilla extract. _____ in the milk. _____ the flour, baking powder, and salt
    4   5   6

into a bowl. _____ this to the mixture. _____ well. _____ at 350 degrees for about
                  7   8   9

45 minutes. _____ the cake onto a plate and _____ before icing.
               10   11

EXERCISE 2

You and your friend are making Ann Brennan's yellow cake. Complete the dialogue by asking *how much* or *how many* about the words in the parentheses. Look at the recipe above to answer the questions.

A: We have flour, salt, baking powder, and vanilla extract. What else do we need?

B: Well, we need milk, eggs, sugar, and butter.

A: I'll get them. _How much milk do we need?_
                              milk

B: _____

A: _____
                              eggs

B: _____

A: _____
                              sugar

B: _____

A: _____
                              butter

B: _____

EXERCISE 1

How much do the coins in each picture equal? Write complete sentences.

1. *Two dimes and a nickel equal a quarter.*

2. _____

3. _____

4. _____

5. _____

6. _____

Put the directions for using a washing machine in the correct order.

____ Put detergent in machine.

____ Press "Start."

____ Remove clean clothes.

____ Put dirty clothes in machine.

____ Close machine.

____ Open machine.

__1__ Choose the water temperature you want.

Match the two parts of each sentence to make directions for using a candy machine.

1. Remove ___C___   a. use pennies.

2. Insert _____   b. the correct button.

3. Decide _____   c. the candy.

4. Press _____   d. what you want.

5. Don't _____   e. the coins.

Now write the directions above in the correct order.

1. _Decide what you want._

2. _____

3. _____

4. _____

5. _____

EXERCISE 1

Read the conversation and write the correct words from the choices in parentheses.

Lynn: What do you _____*want to*_____ do today, Keiko?
1 (want/want to)

Keiko: I don't know. First, I _____ do some errands.
2 (need/need to)

I _____ a lot of things. Then I _____
3 (need/need to)   4 (want/want to)
relax. What about you?

Lynn: I _____ some errands too. Let's _____ do
5 (have/have to)   6 (try/try to)
our errands early.

Keiko: Good idea. Then let's go to a movie. How about *The Cowboy Rides Again?*

Lynn: I don't really _____ westerns. How about a comedy?
7 (like/like to)

I _____ laugh tonight.
8 (need/need to)

Keiko: OK. I _____ the newspaper. Let's _____
9 (have/have to)   10 (try/try to)
find a good comedy.

Lynn: OK. And we can _____ that new Italian restaurant for dinner.
11 (try/try to)

I always _____ eat at new restaurants.
12 (like/like to)

EXERCISE 2

Match the words on the left with the responses on the right.

1. I'm hungry. _c_

2. Sorry. I don't have any change. ____

3. Let's get something to eat. ____

4. Here you are. ____

5. How much is a soda? ____

6. Do you have change for a dollar? ____

a. Good idea.

b. Thank you very much.

c. Let's get a snack.

d. Yes, I think so.

e. Thanks anyway.

f. 75 ¢.

It is Monday, 11:00 A.M. Look at Tony's schedule. Then complete the sentences.

Mon.	Tues.	Wed.	Thurs.	Fri.	Sat.	Sun.
10:00 class 12:00 have lunch with Carlos 7:00 go to the movies	Work all day!	3:00 see the doctor	Visit my Aunt Maria	Paint the kitchen	Go to New York!	

1. After class, Tony _is having lunch with Carlos._

2. Tonight, _____

3. Tomorrow, _____

4. On Wednesday, _____

5. On Thursday, _____

6. On Friday, _____

7. This weekend, _____

Read this note from Olga's friend. There are six mistakes. Find the mistakes and correct them.

Dear Olga,
               doing
  What are you ~~do~~ during the school break? Do you stay in Dallas? I want visit you in Dallas. I need relax. I don't want to travel. I want stay with you and talk. Let think about our vacation. OK?

          See you soon,
          Mariny

EXERCISE 1

Circle the correct response.

1. How about the Star Restaurant?

   a. Fine, thanks.

   (b.) That's fine.

2. Are you ready to order?

   a. Thank you.

   b. Yes, I am.

3. What kind do you have?

   a. Well done.

   b. Vanilla, cherry, and chocolate.

4. What would you like?

   a. Vanilla ice cream, please.

   b. Medium, please.

5. I'd like some orange juice.

   a. A cup or a bowl?

   b. Large or small?

6. How would you like your hamburger?

   a. Rare.

   b. Yes, I would.

7. What's the special?

   a. $8.75.

   b. A cheeseburger and French fries.

8. How much is a small salad?

   a. It's very good.

   b. 75¢.

9. Anything to drink?

   a. No, thank you.

   b. Small, please.

10. Anything else?

   a. No, thank you.

   b. Apple and cherry.

EXERCISE 2

Which word doesn't belong? Cross it out.

1. pie   cake   ice cream   ~~salad~~

2. chocolate   vanilla   strawberry   tuna

3. well done   bad   rare   medium

4. soda   juice   tea   soup

5. large   apple   medium   small

6. salad   glass   cup   bowl

7. nickel   dime   coin   quarter

Read the menu and the check below. Then complete the conversation.

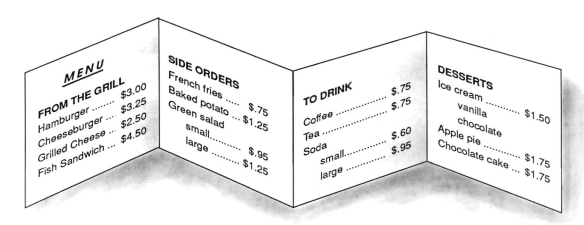

Waiter: Can I help you?

Tony: *Yes, I'd like a cheeseburger and French fries.*

Waiter: Anything to drink?

Tony: _____

Waiter: Large or small?

Tony: _____

Waiter: Would you like dessert?

Tony: _____

Waiter: Anything else?

Tony: _____

Now complete the check.

CHECK

1	cheeseburger	3	25
			75
1	small soda		
		1	75
	Total	6	35